STAGE 2

SECRETS

BY TONY BRADMAN AND JANICE PIMM

ILLUSTRATED BY BRIONY MAY SMITH, MARK LONG, ALESSIA TRUNFIO AND PATRICK MILLER

OXFORD
UNIVERSITY PRESS

CONTENTS

A NERVOUS SPY

BY TONY BRADMAN

ILLUSTRATED BY BRIONY MAY SMITH

BEFORE READING

Setting the scene

A spy is someone who works in secret to get information that is supposed to be kept hidden. Spies have to be extremely careful not to get caught because they would be in serious trouble with the people they are spying on. The 'spy' in this story accidentally comes across something that should have been secret and then has to decide what to do with the information.

Prepare to read

Read the first page of the story, page 7.

Use the expert tip:

■ **Explore vocabulary – clarify words and phrases**

Challenge word

impulsively

Find this word on page 12. Can you work out what it means?

Try making up a sentence of your own using the word 'impulsively'.

A NERVOUS SPY

"Are you all right, Nadiya?" said Mum. "Is everything OK at school? You certainly haven't been your normal cheerful self for the last couple of days."

"I'm fine, Mum," said Nadiya, as she clambered out of the car. "See you later."

Mum smiled as she drove away while Nadiya headed for the school gates. Pausing only to say a brief hello to her friends, Nadiya headed straight inside the building.

Usually, Nadiya would have lingered in the playground, chattering excitedly, but today she didn't feel much like talking.

She sat in a dark corner of the cloakroom and brooded. There *was* something wrong, but she didn't want to tell anyone about it. At the beginning of the week her teacher, Mr Jackson, had told the class they would have a grammar test on Friday.

"It will be challenging," he'd said. "The questions will really stretch your brains!"

Nadiya liked Mr Jackson because he was humorous and his lessons were always interesting. However, she didn't like tests – they made her feel nervous. Grammar definitely wasn't her favourite subject, either. What if she got all the questions wrong?

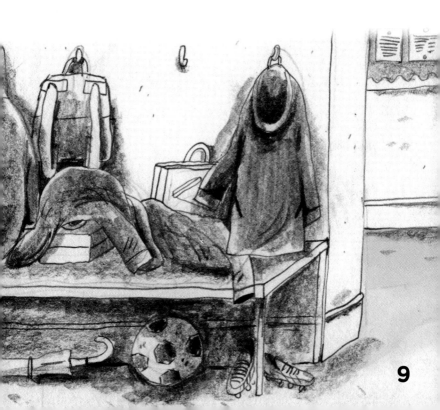

When the school bell rang Nadiya jumped, realizing she was about to be late for class. She hurried out of the cloakroom and down the empty corridor, passing the head teacher's room, the school office and the photocopier in its cubby-hole.

Somebody had dropped a couple of sheets of paper near the photocopier. Nadiya picked them up, thinking she would hand them in at the office – but then she glanced at them and stopped.

Her eyes suddenly grew wide. The first sheet was headed 'Friday Grammar Test – Questions', and the second said 'Friday Grammar Test – Answers.' Nadiya took a deep breath and felt her face flush. She didn't read any more, and quickly folded the papers so she couldn't see what was printed on them.

They were secret and she knew she should take them to Mr Jackson – but she didn't.

Impulsively, Nadiya stuffed the papers deep down into her school bag. She could look at them later ...

She didn't, though. It was impossible to get the papers out of her bag during lessons. What if a friend spotted what she was doing? What if Mr Jackson or another teacher saw her reading them? Nowhere was safe; there were always people around.

Nadiya felt increasingly anxious all morning. She carried her school bag with her everywhere, even into the playground, holding it close to her chest. Every time someone approached her, she jumped nervously. Whenever one of her friends tried to talk to her, she flinched. This must be how it is for spies, she thought; even the cleverest spies must always feel they're about to be caught.

Nadiya felt terribly guilty, too. If she looked at the test questions and answers she could do brilliantly in the test, and that would be fantastic. However, it would also be cheating, and that wouldn't be fantastic at all. What's more, she would have to keep the secret forever and she didn't think she could bear being praised for good marks she hadn't earned fairly.

By the end of break, Nadiya had made her mind up. She went back to the cloakroom and took the papers out of her bag. Then she went to find Mr Jackson.

"Er ... Mr Jackson, I found these on the floor by the photocopier," she said. "I know what they are – but I promise I didn't look at them, honest!"

"Thanks, Nadiya," said Mr Jackson. "I'm sure you didn't!"

Nadiya smiled. She somehow felt that she had just passed one test.

The next one couldn't be anywhere near as hard ...

Secrets and Spies!

BY TONY BRADMAN
ILLUSTRATED BY MARK LONG

BEFORE READING

Setting the scene

Did you know that spies are not just characters from films or stories? There are real people whose job it is to be a spy. If you were going to be a professional spy, what sort of skills, equipment and training would you need? Read this text to find out all about real-life spies.

Prepare to read

Did you know that there are real people who work as spies?

Use the expert tips:

- **Ask a question** What skills do you need if you want to become a spy? Look for key information that will help you answer this question as you continue reading this text.

- **Summarize the text** Read page 19. Identify the key information on this page about a job that a real spy might do.

Challenge word

furthermore

Find this word on page 25. Can you work out what it means?

When do you think this word might come in useful?

Secrets and Spies!

We've all seen spies in the movies – amazing characters who have an incredible range of skills, a vast collection of gadgets, and use them all in their battles against villains. Spies in real life aren't like this, of course ... or are they?

A real spy is unlikely to be involved in a movie-style car chase but their secret work is very important. A spy might find out if her country's enemies are about to launch an attack or hack her country's computers.

Spy skills

Spies in films often draw far too much attention to themselves. The skills real spies need are:

Blending in

A spy needs to look and behave exactly like the people she is living or working among so nobody suspects she is a spy.

Learning languages

Spies need to be fluent speakers of the language of the country they're working in.

Sorting information

Many spies work in offices where their role is to sort information from different sources and decide what is important.

Computer skills

Increasingly, government spy agencies need to prevent 'cyber attacks' – attacks on a country's computer systems. People with high-level computer skills are essential for this.

Gadgets

The modern spy has a range
of technical gadgets.

Spy cams

Tiny spy cameras can be hidden
in all sorts of objects such as:

buttons

pens

key-rings

Document scanners

A document scanner can be hidden
inside a pen. The spy can move
the pen across a page right
under someone's nose!

Coins

Hollow coins have been used for many years to transport secret messages. Today, a spy might use one to hide a micro memory card containing valuable information.

Spy drones

Drones fly in the air and can carry live-feed video cameras, microphones and heat sensors. High-tech cameras can scan entire cities or zoom in to read tiny print.

a drone with a camera

Recruiting a spy

Imagine that a spy agency needs to recruit a new spy. Here's the advertisement it might post:

CENTRAL **ESPIONAGE** AGENCY

Could you be a spy?
We are seeking a new spy to join our busy team.
Our ideal candidate will:
- be highly intelligent
- have first-class computer skills
- speak several languages
- be physically fit.

Full training will be given. The job is mainly based at our city offices but you will also be required to work in different countries.

Please send letters of application to:
Ms Daintree, Central Espionage Agency,
The Secret House, Grover Street, Uptown City.

Glossary
espionage spying

Corner House
2 River Street
Great Spey
GS23 8QM
21st October 2017

Ms Daintree,
Central Espionage Agency,
The Secret House,
Grover Street,
Uptown City

Dear Ms Daintree,

I am writing to apply for the position of Spy at Central Espionage Agency.

I believe I am the perfect candidate because I have all the skills you require.

I am brilliant at computing and came top of my year at university. Furthermore, I recently won a prize for the fastest person to decode a secret message.

I speak Spanish and German fluently. In addition, I am currently learning Hungarian. Moreover, as my parents travelled for work, I lived in several different countries during my childhood.

I am extremely fit, as I run marathons in my spare time.

In conclusion, I am eager to learn more about the job and am available for interview at any time. I look forward to hearing from you.

Yours sincerely,

Daniel Edwards

Daniel Edwards

I KNOW
A SECRET
BY TONY BRADMAN

BEFORE READING

Setting the scene

The poem in this text describes what it is like when you are trying to keep a secret. The poet has chosen words very carefully to help you form images in your mind as you are reading. You can use your imagination to decide who might be saying the words of this poem.

Prepare to read

Have you ever had an exciting secret to keep? Was it easy or hard not to tell?

Read the first two verses of the poem on page 29.

Use the expert tip:

■ **Visualize – form a picture in your mind** Who do you imagine is saying these words?

Challenge word

blurt it out
Find these words on page 31. Can you work out what they mean?

I KNOW A SECRET

I know a secret.
I've promised not to tell.
I'm sure I won't let it out,
I could keep lots more as well.

I know a secret.
I've got to hold it in ...
But that won't be a problem!
It's a battle I can win.

I know a secret.
I can feel it deep inside.
It's stretching and it's straining,
It doesn't want to hide.

I know a secret.
You can see it in my eyes.
Don't ask me where I heard it,
I'll have to tell you lies!

I know a secret.
I'm scared I'll blurt it out.
I can hardly keep my mouth closed,
I want to scream and shout!

I know a secret ...
And now you know it too,
But I'm sure it's still a secret,
Just between me and you.

I know a secret...
And so do all our friends,
And your mum and dad and granny,
A list that never ends!

I *knew* a secret,
But now it's everywhere,
And people call me blabbermouth.
The truth is hard to bear!

About Tony Bradman

Tony Bradman has written hundreds of stories and poems for children and teenagers. Here, he tells us what drew him to writing.

"I discovered books and stories when I was at primary school and soon became the kind of person who reads all the time! I dimly remember liking *Thomas the Tank Engine* books when I was very young, but it was J R R Tolkien's *The Hobbit* that really got me hooked when a great teacher called Mr Smith read it to my class. I was soon reading all the time. I loved words and language."

"By the time I was a teenager I'd pretty much decided I wanted to be a writer. I went to university and became a journalist after I left. It was when I became a dad and started reading books to my daughter that I remembered my love of children's books.

I was soon writing my own stories and poems and things went well. The first book I had published was a collection of poems for young children called *Smile, Please!* Since then I've written over a hundred stories for children and teenagers including many stories for *Project X*, published by Oxford University Press.

Why do I write so much? It all comes down to one thing – a love of reading. I don't think that's ever going to change!"

A SPY ON MALIA

BY JANICE PIMM
ILLUSTRATED BY ALESSIA TRUNFIO

BEFORE READING

Setting the scene

Malia is the beautiful planet where the twins, Anya and Sami, live. You first met them in the story *Saving Planet Malia* (in the book *Wild Water*) when they courageously saved their planet. Unfortunately, the danger hasn't gone away and Anya and Sami are about to face a new threat.

Prepare to read

Use the expert tips:

■ **Think and remember** Think back to the story *Saving Planet Malia*. What do you know already about what the planet is like? Why is Malia under threat? What are Anya and Sami like?

■ **Make connections – search for clues** Read this sentence and work out who the pronoun 'I' refers to:

Malia is the beautiful planet where I live with my twin brother, Sami.

Compare this sentence with the first sentence of 'Setting the scene'. Can you spot what has changed?

Challenge word

lately

Find this word on page 38. Can you work out what it means?

A SPY ON MALIA
Chapter 1

It was my brother, Sami, who heard it first. We were about to dive into the river for our early morning swim when Sami clutched my arm and hissed, "Anya! What's that?"

I couldn't hear anything so I shook Sami's arm away impatiently. I loved swimming in the cool, clear river and I couldn't wait to get started – but then I heard the sound too, a long low moan coming from behind the bushes on the riverbank.

At one time, back when our Planet Malia felt safe, Sami and I would have raced towards the bush to find out what was making the noise. However, things had happened on Malia to make us fearful.

Our Zilean neighbours had been attacking our planet for months. Lately, the attacks had grown worse. Night after night, we'd lain in our beds trembling while Zilean shuttles thundered overhead. Then, for the past three days, the attacks had stopped. You'd have thought we'd be relieved, but the silence made us anxious.

So when we heard the moaning noise,
Sami and I waited with our nerves jangling,
until the sound grew louder and more urgent
and we realized it was someone groaning
in pain.

"Come on, we need to look," Sami said,
grabbing my hand and pulling
me round the bush.

A Zilean man lay on the ground, his face twisting in agony. He had a deep wound in one leg and his knee was bent at a very odd angle. When he saw us, his eyes widened in terror like a wild animal caught in a trap.

"What's he doing here?" I cried. "I bet he's a spy! Quick – let's get someone to lock him up before he does anything dangerous!"

"Anya!" Sami said. "He's not dangerous right *now*. He needs our help – urgently!"

Of course, I thought, *Sami's right*. I hurried to find leaves to heal the wound while Sami collected wood to make a splint. As I laid the healing leaves on his leg, the Zilean man cried out in pain. Then he breathed a sigh of relief.

"Does that feel better?" I asked. The Zilean man smiled and I was surprised to see how his eyes crinkled upwards at the corners, making him look almost friendly. Maybe he wasn't a spy after all.

Sami handed the Zilean man a bottle of water and the man took a long drink. "Thank you," he said. "I was so thirsty." Then he asked, "Have you got any food? I'm starving!"

I gave him a half-eaten piece of flatbread from my pocket. The man ate greedily.

"I'll go and pick some berries and fruit," said Sami, and he ran off before I could say anything.

The man smiled at me again. "I'm going to take a little rest," he said, closing his eyes. Soon he appeared to be sleeping.

I noticed a piece of paper in the man's pocket and leaned forward to take a closer look. Could it be ... yes it was! A map of Planet Malia!

I sat back, my mind racing. Why was the man carrying a map of our planet? What was he planning?

We need to tell someone urgently, I thought. I had to find Sami.

At that moment, the man's eyes flicked open. He pressed a button on his ring and out shot a thin silver thread. Before I knew what was happening, the thread curled round my ankles and bound them tightly.

I was trapped!

A SPY ON MALIA
Chapter 2

BEFORE READING

Prepare to read

At the end of the first chapter, Anya was trapped. Can you remember how that happened? Where was Anya's brother?

Use the expert tips:

■ **Predict** What do you know about Sami? Look back at pages 39 and 41 to find out about Sami's character. What do you think Sami might do?

■ **Make connections - search for clues** What do you think the Zilean man is planning to do?

Challenge word

grimaced

Find the word on page 49. Can you work out what it means?

Chapter 2

I struggled, trying to to free my ankles from the silver thread, but it was impossible.

"I'd give up if I were you," the man said. "It's Zilean thread. You can't untie it or snap it."

"Let me go!" I cried angrily. "We *helped* you. Why are you doing this?"

Just then, I saw Sami in the distance coming back towards the river, his pockets crammed with berries and fruit. The Zilean man hadn't noticed him. *Don't come close,* I thought. *He'll trap you, too*!

Sometimes, Sami and I understand each other's thoughts without having to speak out loud – but not this time. Sami came bounding up to us and, in a split second, the man shot out another thread and Sami was trapped too.

Sami was pale with shock and I could see the fear in his eyes. Yet he took a few deep breaths and began talking to the man in a calm voice.

"You might as well let us go," Sami began. "You won't be able to walk on that leg for a while ... and Anya will need to find more leaves to change your dressing."

The man tried to move his leg and grimaced in pain. "I can't let you go," he said, almost sadly. "Eat your berries. It's going to be a long day."

I struggled against the thread again. What were the Zileans planning to do? I was restless and angry but all through that long day, Sami stayed calm.

"How did you hurt your leg?" Sami asked, after a while.

"Our plan went wrong," the man replied. "The shuttle was supposed to fly low enough to drop me safely but I fell when I landed."

"What were you planning to do?" Sami asked. The man shook his head. "It's secret," he said.

As the evening shadows lengthened, we noticed the man staring up into the sky towards Planet Zilea.

"Are you thinking about home?" Sami asked.

The man sighed deeply, then began to speak. "Things are very bad on Zilea," he said. "There is little food and no work. No one visits us – everyone comes to Malia. We thought that if we spoiled your planet, people would visit us instead, bringing us food and riches."

"That hasn't worked, has it?" said Sami. "So what's your plan now?"

"Exactly what I'm doing," the man replied. "I'm to find children and hold them prisoner until you Malians agree to help us."

"You don't need to do this!" I cried. "Our people will help Zilea anyway. All you need to do is ask!"

Just then, we heard a babble of voices approaching the river. I knew it was a search party, coming to find us. I could hear our mum and dad among the crowd. The Zilean man looked startled.

"Trust us," said Sami. "We Malians will help you."

The man hesitated.

"It's OK," I said softly.

The Zilean man nodded and pressed the button on his ring. The silver thread unwound from our ankles.

I sighed with relief just as Mum came rushing towards us.

"We've been looking for you everywhere!" she said.

Sami stood up. "We need to help the Zileans," he said. "It's a long story. Let me explain ..."

The search party fell silent, waiting for Sami to speak further. I stood up, too, and smiled. I knew our people would forgive the Zileans and help when they heard their story. Everything was going to be all right – for all of us.

Bletchley Park

BY JANICE PIMM

BEFORE READING

Setting the scene

When countries are at war with each other, both sides try to find out what the other side is planning. They keep the plans secret by using complicated codes and that is when the real-life spies get to work, trying to crack the codes. During the Second World War, hundreds of code-breakers worked in secret at 'Station X', deciphering secret messages.

Prepare to read

Read page 57.

Use the expert tips:

■ **Use text structures, features and language**
Did anything that you have read so far confuse you? Remember, you can use features in the text to help you understand. Use the glossary to find out what 'allies' means.

■ **Ask a question** Do you have any questions that you would like to find the answer to?

Here is an example: Where was 'Station X'?

Challenge word

otherwise
Find the word on page 63. Can you work out what it means? Try making up a sentence of your own using the word 'otherwise'.

Bletchley Park

Bletchley Park is a **mansion** house in Buckinghamshire, England. During World War Two, it was the place where Britain's code-breakers cracked many important secret codes used by the Germans and Japanese. The Germans used the secret codes to send messages about war plans to their army, navy and air-force. Cracking the codes meant that Britain and its **allies** knew the German plans. Then they could work out how to stop them.

Top secret

All work at Bletchley Park was top secret. The mansion was in a good location because it was in the countryside, away from London which was the main German target. Bletchley Park was referred to as 'Station X'.

The workers at Bletchley Park worked in huts set up on the lawns. Different groups of people worked in each hut, depending on the job they did. For security reasons, these groups of people were only referred to by hut numbers.

Who worked at Bletchley Park?

Many of the people who worked at Bletchley Park were top mathematicians and skilled problem-solvers. Everyone had to keep their work top secret, not even telling their families and friends what they were doing. Even after the war ended in 1945, people rarely talked about the work they did at Bletchley Park.

World War Two was fought between 1939 and 1945. On one side were Britain, America, France and their allies – and later, Russia. On the other side were Germany, Italy, Japan and their allies.

Enigma

The Enigma Code was probably the most important code to be broken at Bletchley Park. The Germans thought the code, created by Enigma machines, was totally secure.

Thousands of **wireless operators** listened in secret to Germany's coded messages. The messages were then sent to Bletchley Park to be decoded.

Enigma machine

The Enigma machine looked like an oversized typewriter.

How it worked

1. The 'sender' typed a letter on the keyboard.

2. The signal passed to 'rotors' that were like wheels with tangled wire inside. The rotors turned and changed the letter to a new letter.

3. A signal was then sent back through the machine.

4. The signal passed through the keyboard again and lit up the new letter on the light board.

5. The sender sent the coded message using **Morse code**.

6. The '**receiver**' used a machine set up with the same pattern. The receiver keyed in the coded message and the real message lit up.

The 'Bombe'

The Engima machine could create 150 million million million options for each letter! At first, people decoded the scrambled messages by hand and brain, but this took a long time. Then the mathematicians Alan Turing and Gordon Welchman developed a machine called the 'Bombe' which helped to unscramble the code much more quickly. This was important because the Germans changed the Enigma code every day.

How did the code-breakers help?

The decoded messages were sent to army and navy commanders, providing very useful information.

For example, the messages helped the British track German U-boats (submarines) in the Atlantic Ocean. This meant they could stop the German U-boats from sinking ships bringing food supplies to Britain from the USA.

The British needed to keep it secret that they had broken Enigma, otherwise the Germans would use another code. So the British pretended their information had come from an imaginary spy in Germany, code-named Boniface.

Other code-breakers

As the war continued, Germany and Japan developed more complex codes and **ciphers**. Britain then had to develop machines to help crack these. This led to the design and construction of 'Colossus' – the world's first semi-programmable electronic computer.

Glossary

allies   friends or friendly countries

cipher   a secret or disguised way of writing; a code

mansion   a large house

Morse code   a way of sending messages using short dots and long dashes

receiver   someone information is sent to

wireless operator   person who operated radios during World War Two

Digging up the Past

BY TONY BRADMAN

BEFORE READING

Setting the scene

Is it possible for us to know what life on Earth was like thousands of years ago? One way to find out is to start digging down into the ground, searching for evidence buried below the surface that gives clues about the past. This isn't like digging in the garden or on the beach. Read on to find out about the special skills, knowledge and tools that you need for this type of work.

Prepare to read

Read page 67. Use the expert tips to help you understand the information you have read:

■ **Explore vocabulary – clarify words and phrases** and **Use text structures, features and language** Use the glossary and 'Did you know?' box to help you understand the word 'archaeologist'.

Do you know any other words ending in –ologist?

■ **Make connections – search for clues** Look back at the phrase 'artefacts people left behind'. Were these artefacts just chucked away with the rubbish? Were they precious objects that were buried with people? Look out for clues as you are reading.

Challenge word

alternatively
Find this word on page 68. Can you work out what it means? Try making up a sentence using 'alternatively'.

Digging up the Past

When you go to a museum, you might see all sorts of amazing things – Roman coins, Iron Age swords, Greek vases, Saxon jewellery. These items have usually been found by **archaeologists**. Archaeologists study the past by looking for and examining the **artefacts** people left behind long ago. Such objects can tell us an amazing amount about how ancient people lived.

DID YOU KNOW ?

The word archaeology comes from two Greek words – *archaios*, meaning 'ancient', and *logos*, meaning 'study' – so archaeology is the study of the past.

Where to dig

Archaeologists begin by finding interesting sites to dig. Some sites are obvious because ancient structures are visible, such as Stonehenge in Britain or the Pyramids in Egypt. Alternatively, archaeologists study the land, often using aerial photographs.

DID YOU KNOW?

In 2015 scientists thought they had detected massive stones close to Stonehenge. The 'stones' turned out to be pits filled with chalk. Huge wooden poles had once stood in the pits. This showed that the pits were probably part of a timber monument built 4500 years ago!

Stonehenge

Excavating a site

Once a site is identified, archaeologists explore it very carefully. This is called excavation. Rather than digging huge holes, archaeologists excavate in layers. First, the top layer of soil is removed by machine or by hand. Then each layer of soil is removed before moving on to the next. Historical artefacts can be found in different layers, so it is important to work slowly and carefully.

Tools

Archaeologists use spades, small hand shovels, spoons, knives and brushes. They use sieves to sift the soil. The most important tool in the archaeologist's kit is probably the four-pointed hand trowel.

four-pointed hand trowel

small brush

For the delicate work of cleaning away soil, archaeologists use small brushes.

Archaeologists often dig up tiny fragments of artefacts. They then spend a lot of time sorting the fragments. During this process, they might use tiny tools to clean the fragments such as a small toothbrush or dentist's pick.

Recording and dating

Archaeologists keep detailed records of each layer of the excavation site. They record exactly where artefacts were found and their depth from the surface.

They also work out and record *when* each artefact was made. This is known as **dating** the artefact. Dating can be done in different ways.

Matching artefacts	Archaeologists compare artefacts with objects in nearby museums that have a known date.
Depth found	Archaeologists look at objects in the same layer which have a date. Coins are very useful for this!
Carbon dating	Archaeologists can date remains (such as wood, charcoal, leather or bones) which contain a substance called carbon.

What do artefacts tell us?

Artefacts can tell us how people lived at certain times in history.

For example, bones of deer tell us that people were hunters; fish bones tell us that they were fishermen; bones of cattle and sheep tell us that they were farmers.

animal bone

arrow tip

Tools such as arrow tips tell us that people were hunters. Knives and **grinding stones** tell us how they prepared food.

Images on jewellery, pots and ornaments often tell us a lot about people and how they lived.

Ancient footprints

Archaeologists have even found ancient footprints, usually by rivers or lakes. In Kenya there are some footprints of our distant ancestors – it's thought they're one and a half million years old. Ancient footprints have also been discovered in Britain. On one site in Norfolk there are so many, it looks like the tracks of a whole family.

Ancient footprints in Norfolk

Glossary

archaeologist   someone who studies history by finding and examining ancient objects

artefact   something people made, used and left behind

to date   in archaeology, to work out when something was made

grinding stone   a stone used to grind wheat into flour

DANGER IN THE FOREST

BY TONY BRADMAN
ILLUSTRATED BY PATRICK MILLER

BEFORE READING

Setting the scene

Thousands and thousands of years ago, early humans lived in caves, hunted for deer in the forests and gathered shellfish from by the sea. They didn't have permanent homes because they moved when the weather got bad, following the animals they were hunting. This story imagines what life was like for our ancient ancestors.

Prepare to read

Read page 77 and think about what you have found out about the story so far.

Use the expert tips:

■ **Read it again** Look back to help you answer these questions: who is in the story? Where are they?

■ **Make connections – search for clues** Are there any clues about when in history this story takes place? Look at 'Setting the scene' and the illustration on page 77. What can you work out?

Challenge word

stomped

Find this word on page 83. Can you work out what it means? What does it tell you about the character's feelings?

DANGER IN THE FOREST

Chapter 1

It was early in the morning, the pale sun was rising over the sea and Father was getting ready to go hunting. Boy stood watching him from the mouth of the cave in the cliff where they had spent the last few days. Below them stretched a wide sandy beach.

"Why can't I go with you, Father?" said Boy. "It's just not fair."

"You know why, Boy," said Father. He tucked an axe into his belt and picked up his spear. Both had blades made of chipped flint, which were tied to their wooden shafts with strips of dried hide. "You are not yet ready to follow the hunting trail."

"But I *am* ready!" said Boy, frowning. "I am eight summers old ..."

"Father is right," said a voice behind them. Mother had come out of the cave now as well. Boy opened his mouth to argue, but Mother held up her hand to silence him.

"Your day will come," she said. "Besides, I want you to look after Little One."

"Oh no, do I have to?" Boy groaned. Little One was his younger sister. She was only four summers old, always happy and smiling – and full of mischief. Boy enjoyed playing with her sometimes, but looking after her on his own was tedious. She was asleep inside the cave, curled up on some furs beside the fire.

"Yes, you do," said Mother. "I need to find as much food as I can today. You know that will be hard if I have Little One with me." Mother smiled and ruffled Boy's hair. "Don't look so glum, Boy. I promise we'll be back before the sun sets."

"We will have meat to cook when we get home, so be sure to keep the fire going," said Father, grinning at him. "I feel sure in my heart that I will kill a deer for us, and when I return I will tell you the story of the hunt. That will help you to learn."

They both set off. Father went one way up the beach, towards the gap in the cliffs that would lead to the forest. Mother went the other way with her basket, heading to places where she could find mussels and small crabs and dig for shellfish.

81

Boy sat down on a rock. He was so angry and frustrated he felt like crying. If only there was some way he could prove that he was ready to go hunting – but how? The summer was almost over, and the family would be leaving before it turned cold and the leaves fell. Mother and Father needed to collect a lot of food for the long journey to the Warm Lands, and that meant they would make him look after Little One all the time.

His sister woke up a while later, and came out of the cave. "Play with me, Boy," she said, putting her arms round him from behind. Irritated, Boy shook her off and stood up.

"Leave me alone!" he said grumpily, and stomped off down the beach to the sea. Little One called out, but he ignored her and threw pebbles into the waves.

Soon he felt guilty for being horrible, and went back up the beach.

"Little One!" he called out. "I'm sorry. I will play with you now!"

There was no answer, and Boy thought she must have returned to the cave so he went inside too. The fire was still burning – but the cave was empty.

Little One had gone.

DANGER IN THE FOREST
Chapter 2

BEFORE READING

Prepare to read

What was the awful thing that had happened at the end of Chapter 1?

Use the expert tips:

■ **Predict** What sort of danger is Little One in? Think about what you already know about when and where this story is set.

■ **Make connections – search for clues** Read page 87. Which phrase tells you how Boy is feeling?

Respond to the story

Can you imagine how he is feeling? Have you ever felt like that?

Challenge word

whimpered

Find this word on page 92. Can you work out what it means?

What does it tell you about how Little One is feeling and thinking?

Chapter 2

Boy looked up and down the beach, but there was no sign of his sister. He felt sick with worry; Little One might be in danger. He had to find her before something terrible happened – and before Mother and Father came back.

Suddenly, he noticed that Little One had left some small footprints in the sand. Boy grabbed the spear Father had made for him and set off to follow them. The tracks took him along the beach, to the gap between the cliffs that led to the forest.

It was dark under the trees, and Boy couldn't see Little One anywhere. The ground was baked hard and covered in old leaves, so there were no more footprints. Boy called out her name – "Little One! Where are you?" – but there was no answer.

He couldn't give up, though. So he looked closely at the ground, and saw some faint signs – flattened leaves that might have been squashed by his sister's feet. He followed them, and saw other things – a trampled flower, a snapped branch, leaves bent back on a bush.

After a while he came to a clearing. A huge tree had fallen in the winter, leaving a big hole like a cave in the ground under its roots. Little One was sitting in the hole and talking quietly.

"Look what I've found, Boy!" she said. "They're so pretty, aren't they?"

She was holding a bundle of grey and white fur. There were two more bundles of fur beside her in the hole. All three were making yipping noises. They had blue eyes and pink tongues, and their tiny white teeth were as sharp and pointed as Mother's bone needles.

"What are you doing, Little One?" said Boy, horrified. "Put it down! Those are wolf cubs! Come on, we don't want to be here when their mother gets back."

Suddenly, Boy heard something, and he slowly turned round. Mother Wolf was staring at him with cold eyes, a low growl rumbling deep in her throat. The thick fur on the back of her neck was bristling, and she was creeping towards them. Her teeth were as white as those of her cubs, but they were longer – and sharper.

Little One dropped the cub and whimpered in fear. Boy pulled her out of the hole and shoved her behind him. Then he started backing away from Mother Wolf, pointing his spear at her, making sure he held on to Little One. Mother Wolf watched every step, and followed them, her growling getting deeper and deeper.

They came to the edge of the clearing. "RUN!" said Boy, and they dashed through the forest hand in hand. Mother Wolf pursued them and got close enough to snap at their heels.

Little One screamed, and Boy picked
her up and ran until he felt his chest would
burst. At last he crashed out of the trees and
glanced over his shoulder.

Mother Wolf paused at the edge of the
forest. For a while she stared after them with
her steely golden eyes – then abruptly, she
turned tail and headed back into the shadows.

Later, Little One told Mother and Father about finding the wolf cubs and how Boy had saved her from Mother Wolf. Then Father asked Boy how he had managed to track Little One through the forest, and Boy told him what he had done.

"You did well, Boy," said Father. "Perhaps I will take you hunting next time."

Boy smiled.

Three days later, they set off for the Warm Lands. Boy looked back at the footprints they left in the sand. He wondered who else might come to this beach – but he would never know ...